Garden Birthday

story by Deborah Kaye
illustrations by Richard Bernal

HARCOURT BRACE & COMPANY

Orlando Atlanta Austin Boston San Francisco Chicago Dallas New York
Toronto London

Carrot cake.

Fruit cake.

Bug cake.

Grass cake.

Mud cake.

Yes! Birthday cake!